INTRODUCTION

Your brain is divided into two halves: the right half of your brain learns facts and figures and the left half houses your creativity. You work hard to develop the right half of your brain in school, but sometimes the left half gets ignored. So this book is full of games that will help you to explore every corner of your imagination.

Don't worry if some of the games seem crazy. Just jump in with both feet and give them a try. The games can be played anywhere there's a little bit of room, with lots of friends, or as few as two people. And the best thing is that you can never lose! It's not a competition, it's an opportunity to discover all the wild places your imagination can take you.

Remember, your creativity knows no limits!

OUT OF A HAT

Do you have a favorite hat? How do you feel when you wear it? Sometimes a hat can define the way you walk, stand, sit, or act.

- Find a bunch of old hats and put them in a big bag.
- Without looking, you and a friend should each pick a hat from the bag and put it on.
- Look at yourselves in a mirror so you can see how the hats make you look.
- When you've decided how the hats make you feel, make up a scene to show each other your new personalities.

SPARKS: *Try to react to your friend's new personality in your own new personality. How would these new characters get along? Would they be friends? What would they talk about? What would they do?*

Do you talk with your hands? Simple gestures can add a lot of meaning to what you say.

- Have a friend put his hands behind his back.
- Stand behind him and slip your arms under his, so it looks like your arms are now your friend's arms.
- Ask your friend to start telling a story that you both know.
- While your friend speaks you move your arms and hands to go with the story.

SPARKS: *Did the arm movements get bigger when the story got more exciting? Now try demonstrating a recipe. Or giving directions. If you don't have an audience, try this game looking in the mirror.*

CREATING A MONSTER

If you were a mad scientist what kind of monster wou you create?

- As you announce each characteristic your monster will have, your friend should take on that trait.
- When you are satisfied with your creation, flip the switch and make it come to life.
- Your friend must decide how the monster will behave with all the traits you have given it.

SPARKS: *Can your monster speak? What would your monster say on its first day of life? What is the monster's name? Try acting out a scene where the monster meets the thing that it is afraid of. Have the scientist help the monster feel better.*

BUTTERFLY TALK

Different people have different rhythms to their speech. Some are fast, rapid-fire speakers. Others are slow and lilting.

- Think of different animals and what speech patterns would fit their personalities.
- How would a butterfly talk? How about a turtle? A hummingbird? A snake?
- You and a friend take turns adopting different speech patterns and see if the other can guess what animal you've become.
- Talk about the weather, or anything else that won't provide any clues to your identity.

SPARKS: *If you get really good at this, try speaking in only numbers instead of using real sentences. Can your friend still guess what you are just by the tone of your voice?*

What do you do when you feel sad? When someone sings a song about how sad they are it's called "singing the blues."

- Think of something that makes people sad and make up a song about it.
- Try to make up a simple rhyme and turn it into your chorus.
- Then just dive into the first verse!
- Put it to any kind of tune you want.

SPARKS: *Try singing the same lyrics you make up to different tunes and rhythms. Sing it as a country western song, or try a rap or an opera version.*

PLAY THE PART

WHAT IF . . .

6

What would happen if Goldilocks met up with the three little pigs?

- Pick familiar characters from different stories and think about how they might react to one another if they met.

- What would they talk about? Where would they meet? How could they help each other?

- Try lots of different characters: Frankenstein and Little Red Riding Hood, Little Bo Peep and the Wolfman, the Wicked Witch of the West and Godzilla.

- Get up and become the characters!

SPARKS: *Don't rehearse or plan what you are going to say to each other. Decide who will play each character and where they will meet, then jump right in! Try to give your story a problem and a solution, and be sure to give it an ending.*

GET IT IN GEAR

Can you and a friend work together like a well-oiled machine?

- Pretend that you are one small moving part of a very large machine.
- Make up a motion that you can repeat over and over again.
- Have your friend become another part of the machine that moves when it comes into contact with your part of the machine.
- Next, try adding a sound to your motion. Be sure it is one you can repeat over and over.
- How long can your machine run smoothly?

SPARKS: *Be sure to keep your movements exactly the same each time. Slowly begin to make the machine operate faster, building the pace of your movement and volume of the sound until the machine explodes!*

Have a friend choose an object from around the house.

- No matter what the object is, you must talk for one minute about how this would be a very important item to have if you were stranded on a deserted island.

- Your friend should time you—remember, only one minute, and it has to be a good reason!

SPARKS: *Keep in mind that there isn't any electricity on a deserted island. If your friend picks an object that needs to be plugged in, you'll have to do some creative thinking about how to use that object on your island.*

How much energy does it take to walk down the street? To move a chair? To lift a hundred-pound weight? Energy is what makes anything go.

- Move your body as if you are fueled by one penny.
- Your friend then builds on that motion as if she is fueled by one nickel.
- Continue back and forth, being fueled by a dime, quarter, and dollar.
- Keep in mind that the movement should get bigger and be related to the previous movement as the money amount increases.

SPARKS: *Make your movements interesting. Use your arms and head and legs! Try other amounts of money like 37¢ or 89¢. How is a $1 movement different from a 99¢ movement? What about $10, $100, or $1,000?*

Did you ever notice how the tone of your voice adds as much to your message as the words you say?

- Listen to a news broadcast on the radio.
- How does the announcer use his or her voice to help make the information clear? How does the announcer change his or her voice for different types of stories?
- Write down your favorite nursery rhymes and present them in the style of a news broadcast.
- Use expressions like, "This just in . . . Mary had a little lamb . . . "

SPARKS: *You might want to have one of the nursery rhymes interrupt another as if it is a late-breaking news flash. Try to make sense of each rhyme and find the information that is the most newsworthy.*

What's your favorite act in a circus? Tightrope walkers? Clowns?

- Make up an act that has never been seen before and would be included in a circus.
- Make sure your act is as crazy as you can possibly make it.
- You might juggle fish while riding a tricycle backwards through a field of flowers. Maybe you train wild ladybugs! What's your hidden talent?

SPARKS: *What do you wear in your act? Is there music in the background? Does your act have a name? How will the ringmaster introduce you?*

ACT YOUR AGE

How many times have you been told to act your age? How do different ages act?

- You and a friend should each write down five different ages on separate slips of paper then fold them up and put them in a bowl.
- Select one of the ages and look at it without showing it to your friend.
- Pretend that you are in the waiting room of a doctor's office.
- Without using words, try to show what age you are, just by the way that you sit and wait.
- Have your friend guess your age.
- Then your friend picks an age out of the bowl and you guess.

SPARKS: *How can you be very clear about your age? What would you do differently if you were five years old than you would if you were seventy-five years old?*

What would it be like to have an extra long neck like a giraffe?

- Pick an animal and try to figure out what it might think about. What does a rhino have on its mind besides its horn? What does a camel think about to keep its mind off water?
- Once you figure it out, stand the way the animal would stand and move the way it would move.
- Then begin to say out loud what the animal has on its mind.
- Have your friend guess what kind of animal you are.

SPARKS: *Play this game again. This time, with your friend, choose one large animal and portray it together. You might be the head and trunk of an elephant while your friend is the body. Work together to show all characteristics of your animal, and have someone else guess what you are.*

Have you ever been so wrapped up in something that you didn't notice what was going on around you?

- Try to walk about ten feet without saying a word or laughing while a friend tries to make you loose your concentration.
- Your friend can do anything she can think of to distract you except touch you. If she does, then you get to start the walk again.

SPARKS: *How do you concentrate when someone is trying to distract you? What can you think about to keep your mind focused, and to keep from laughing?*

How quickly can you communicate how you're feeling without using any words?

- Think of two or more things that you could be feeling at one time. Maybe you're tired and hungry.
- Think about what happened to make you feel that way. Maybe you had a hard day at school and forgot to bring money to buy lunch because you were up all night studying for a test!
- Now, walk into a room using hand and body motions and facial expressions to show how you feel.

SPARKS: *Have your friend watch you walk in and ask him to quickly write down everything that comes to his mind about how you're feeling. Repeat your entrance two or three times. When you're done, check your friend's list and see how you did.*

Just like a muscle, your voice needs to be exercised in order to get the most use out of it.

- Stand with your feet shoulder width apart.
- Imagine yourself starting up the ladder of a slide.
- Take a deep breath and start singing a very low note on the bottom rung.
- As you move up the ladder in your mind your pitch should get higher and it should be at its highest as you reach the top.
- Then bring your pitch back down again as you imagine yourself sliding down the slide.

SPARKS: *Did your voice crack on the way up or down? Did you run out of breath? Try a higher slide, or a bumpy or twisty one.*

How many different versions can there be to one story? What if the story is about a small traffic accident? The drivers of each car involved usually have differing stories, and bystanders often tell completely different stories!

- You and a friend should decide what kind of small accident happened and how many witnesses there were.
- Then split up the roles and take turns telling your versions of the story to a police officer.

SPARKS: *The basic facts of the accident should stay the same but people's stories could vary drastically depending on their perspective. Decide whose story was most creative and whose version was closest to the way things could have really happened. Who makes a reliable witness?*

IMAGINATION STATION

If you were a toaster, how would you stand?

- Pick a familiar machine or appliance.
- Using only your body and some sound effects (no words!), become the machine.
- Have your friend guess what kind of machine you are. Be a coffee pot or a food processor or a computer!

SPARKS: *How does your face look when you are the machine? If you were a refrigerator maybe your face would light up with a happy expression when your door opens. Try to show as many parts of the machine as you can.*

TWO CONVERSATIONS 19

Can you talk and listen at the same time?

- Sit facing a friend.
- Each of you should pick a subject to talk about without letting the other know what it is.
- Then both of you talk at the same time for one minute.
- At the end of one minute share with each other what you heard.

SPARKS: *It's hard to listen and talk at the same time. Could you keep talking without being distracted or laughing? Did your speaking slow down or get faster at times? Try the game again. Pick new subjects to talk about and this time close your eyes. Did you pick up more of the other person's conversation?*

How persuasive can you be?

- Pretend that you are a salesperson and you want very much to sell your goods.
- Decide what you are selling and ask your friend to shop in your store.
- You have to convince your friend that he cannot live without your product. Your friend needs a lot of convincing!

SPARKS: *Do the scene again and allow yourself only two minutes to sell to your friend. Your friend must come up with valid reasons not to buy your product. You must come up with good answers to each reason. See which one of you can work faster!*

Have you ever built something out of blocks? If you have, you know that each block is important and that each must be added one at a time so the whole structure doesn't fall apart. The same is done with a sentence. Each word plays an important role in the overall meaning.

- With a friend, make up a story, each of you offering one word at a time.
- You may choose to start with the word "once." Your friend might add "upon." Then, you might offer "a."
- Soon, you will have strung together words to make sentences and sentences to make a story.

SPARKS: *Try to go as fast as possible. With each new word the story may take some twists and turns that you might not expect. Make sure that your sentences make sense! Give the story a beginning, middle, and end. As a variation, you and your friend could each add a whole sentence at a time.*

Did you ever want to be taller? Or shorter?
- In the time it takes to count to eight, stretch yourself to become as tall as you possibly can.
- Take two more counts to become even taller.
- Take one more count to be the tallest! Don't stand on a chair! Just stretch!
- Now, take eight counts to become as small as you possibly can, then two to be smaller, and one to be smallest.
- Next, try being wide, narrow, or round.

SPARKS: *Remember to use your entire body. Don't worry about doing the same thing as your friend. Your idea about being wide or tall might be different from his. What other extremes can you show with your body? Try slippery, square, or squiggly.*

How many different ways could you use one object?

- Take an everyday object and show how many different things it could become.
- You might use a cup as a hat, a telescope, or a telephone!
- Pass the object back and forth until a player cannot think of a new way to use it.

SPARKS: *Use lots of different objects in this game. It might also be fun to play the game with an object for which you don't know the proper use. Then see if one of your creative uses was correct.*

Have you ever heard the expression "a picture is worth a thousand words"?

- With objects around the house, set up three scenes that will tell a story when seen in order.
- You can use any props that you want. You can become part of each picture too, freezing in three different positions.
- Make it a story with a beginning, middle, and end.

SPARKS: *Have your friend close her eyes until you give the signal to look at the picture. She should see only the completed pictures—none of the set up. Can your friend figure out the story from the three frozen images?*

Are you a fast talker? How fast are you?

- Take your favorite tongue twister and have a friend count how many times you can say it in one minute.
- Then you test your friend. Who can say it more times?

SPARKS: *Concentrate on each word you say. If you make a mistake, start over! Try these twisters: "unique New York," "rubber baby buggy bumpers," and "toy boats."*

What's your favorite comic strip?

- Find a comic strip in a newspaper that has only two characters and act out the scene with a friend.
- What do the characters sound like? How do they walk? Make the comic strip come to life.
- Then do the same scene with a new ending that you and your friend make up.
- What other things might happen to these characters in the same place?

SPARKS: *What might have happened to these characters five minutes before the scene that takes place in the newspaper? Are they in the same place? Are they together? Tell the story before the strip.*

What if someone else was in control of your actions?

- Have a friend begin to tell a story.
- You must act it out at the same time it is being told.
- Make sure that your friend chooses a story that you are not familiar with.
- Make your motions go along with what is being said—no matter how crazy it is!

SPARKS: *Could you keep up with your friend? Remember, the more dramatic the story the better. Use your whole body to tell the story while your friend speaks with great expression.*

With the right tone of voice, can you get a point across no matter what words you're using?

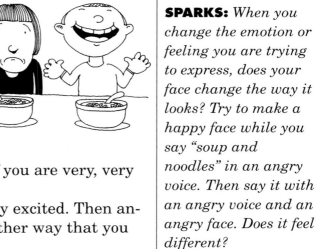

- Say "soup and noodles."
- Then try saying it as if you've just heard the funniest joke in the world!
- Say "soup and noodles" as if you are very, very sad.
- Say it as if you are extremely excited. Then angry, sleepy, jealous, or any other way that you can think of.

SPARKS: *When you change the emotion or feeling you are trying to express, does your face change the way it looks? Try to make a happy face while you say "soup and noodles" in an angry voice. Then say it with an angry voice and an angry face. Does it feel different?*

WHO AM I?

How many people are inside you?

- Think of as many people as you can that your friend would know. Write each person's name on separate slips of paper. Fold them and put them in a hat.
- Pick a name and use your voice and body to become that person. The only thing you can't say is the person's name—your friend has to guess that!
- How many can you guess in three minutes?
- Then see how many your friend can become in the same amount of time.

SPARKS: *Who were the easiest people to become? What makes people memorable? Do they have a certain way of speaking or acting that is all their own?*

Has it ever been so quiet that you could hear your heart beating?

- Sit in a room with a friend and don't make a sound for three minutes.
- Listen as hard as you can for any noises.
- What do you hear? A buzz? A whir? A ding?
- When the time is up write down what you heard without showing your friend. Then compare lists.

SPARKS: *Did both of you hear the same things? Try to figure out what could be making each sound. Now try listening for one more minute, this time with your eyes closed. Did you hear anything new this time?*

Have you ever thrown a ball so hard that you were surprised at how far it went? Imagine if you could put all of that energy into your voice. Nobody would ever complain about not hearing you.

- Stand in a clear area with at least four feet around you.
- Pick up an imaginary ball, about the size of a softball.
- Take a deep breath. Then throw the imaginary ball and at the same time sing a loud "Ah!" and hold it for as long as you can.
- Imagine the ball floating on the air until you run out of breath.

SPARKS: *How far did your ball go? Pay attention to how much breath you release when you throw the ball. Can you control how much breath you let out? Does this make the ball go further? Try the "Ah!" without throwing the ball. Is there a difference in how long you can hold this "Ah"?*

If you were a wok, what would you talk about?

- Without telling your friend what you are, pick an object like a lamp or a washing machine.
- Have your friend start a conversation by asking about your day, and you respond as the object.
- How many questions does your friend have to ask before she can guess what you are?

SPARKS: *What would a lamp complain about? Be creative with your answers. Make your friend ask some tough questions!*

Can you describe a location without saying a word?

- Pick a place—like a park, lake, or baseball field—and don't tell your friend where it is.
- Without speaking, act out an activity that you might do in this place.
- Without guessing out loud, your friend should join you silently, performing another activity that would be done in the same location.

SPARKS: *Was your friend right? How could you have been more clear about where you were? How can you tell if you are inside or outside without speaking? If your environment is a sporting event try to do something other than just playing the game. Sell peanuts! Take tickets!*

RAIN DANCE

34

Have you ever found yourself hoping for rain?

- With a friend, work together to create your own rain dance.
- Will you use music? What will you wear to bring rain? Where will your dance take place? Will you sing?
- Decide why you want the rain to come.
- How fast can you dance without missing a step?

SPARKS: *If the dance that you just made up was to bring rain, what would a dance to stop rain look like? Try making up a dance to prevent floods. Can you do the steps of your rain dance backwards?*

What if your doctor became your teacher? What about a baker or a taxi driver as your teacher? How would they teach? What subjects would seem most important to them?

- Have a friend pretend to be the student while you become the misplaced teacher.
- Your friend should ask you lots of questions!

SPARKS: *Whoever plays the student should ask the teacher lots of questions. Whoever plays the teacher should try to talk and stand and move just as each character would.*

Can you think about two things at once?

- Stand across from your friend and ask, "Where am I?"
- Your friend will make up a place for you to be and you must act out something that would be done in that place.
- Then your friend asks you, "Where am I?"
- While you're still doing your activity, you think of a different place for your friend to be.
- Your friend must now do an activity that would be done in the new place. This cycle continues going back and forth.

SPARKS: *What kind of places did you choose? Classrooms? Doctors' offices? Libraries? Bus stops? Make sure that when you are asked, "Where am I?" you don't say the place where you're pretending to be, but a brand-new place.*

What would the play-by-play report of the race between the tortoise and the hare sound like?

- Become a sports commentator and find out.
- Describe the action as vividly as you can.
- Will you need an instant replay at any point? Are there any interesting statistics you can fill us in on during a lull in the action?
- Be sure to describe the dramatic ending and then wrap up the broadcast with a short recap of the day's events.

SPARKS: *What are some other events you could dramatize? Try a knight battling a dragon. Or a fish and a fisherman. Or a kid playing fetch with a dog.*

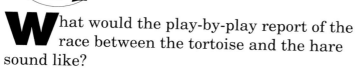

TRUST WALK

Do you really trust your friend?

- Your friend should tie a scarf over your eyes so you absolutely cannot see.
- Have your friend call out the direction you should move, and then you must walk.
- Your friend will tell you when and where to turn so that you don't run into things.
- Each of you should take a turn directing and being directed.

SPARKS: *What was it like not to be able to see where you were going? How did it change the way you walked and the way you held your body?*

Have you ever walked in on a disaster and you can't imagine how it all started?

- You and your friend should act out a scene that is a result of a big disaster. The house might be a mess or maybe it's full of soap suds. Maybe the house has disappeared completely! Make this scene very short.
- Then, flash back to the way the scene may have started.
- Show all of the things that led up to the disaster.

SPARKS: *How many different flashbacks can you come up with for the same disastrous result? Show as many as you can. It's okay if they're totally crazy.*

How closely can you look at an object?
- Find something to look at. It can be any-thing—a chair, a glass, a spot on the floor.
- Choose a corner of the object and look at that even closer.
- Now find a corner of that corner and look even closer!
- Focus in until you can't get any closer!

SPARKS: *What hap-pened to the rest of your body while you were looking at the object? How closely can you zero in on the object? Did it begin to look blurry?*

How many different ways are there to say the same word?

- Think of all the different ways you might say the word "oh."
- Think of all the different reasons to say it.
- How would you say "oh" if you were remembering something you forgot?
- How would it sound if you were surprised? How would it sound if you were frightened?
- You say "oh," giving it a definite inflection.
- Now your friend has to make up a sentence that would follow your "oh."

SPARKS: *Could your friend understand what you meant with each "oh"? Try the same game with other words. Think of all the ways and reasons to say "what," "help," "please," or any other word you choose. Use facial and body expressions to make the meaning behind your word as clear as possible.*

BREAKING THE NEWS 42

Did you ever have to tell someone something that you knew they didn't want to hear?

- Pretend that you have some bad news to tell a friend but you don't know how. Maybe they didn't get the part in the school play, or they have a big piece of spinach stuck to their front tooth!
- Try to think of a gentle way to break the news.
- At the same time your friend will try to change the subject.
- You have three minutes to get the information across.

SPARKS: *Who was successful? Did you break the news? If you're the one trying to change the subject, make sure that you keep up a real conversation. Be sure that what you're saying makes sense.*

Have you ever made something out of clay?

- Pretend you are a lump of clay, then ask a friend to be a sculptor.
- Your friend will move your body into the right position to do something without telling you what that activity is. Your friend might place you in a chair with your hand near your ear as if you're on the phone. You might be placed with your hands over your head and one leg lifted as if you are climbing a tree.
- Once your friend puts you into position, it is your job to figure out what he had in mind and pantomime the activity!

SPARKS: *How could the sculptor have made the activity more clear to you? If you did something other than what the sculptor had in mind, does that mean you were wrong? How many different actions can you come up with from the same starting position?*

BUTTERFINGERS!

Did you ever have a day when everything seemed to go wrong?

- Pretend that you are a bank robber. Have your friend be the bank teller.
- You want to rob the bank, but somehow everything you do goes wrong. Maybe you forgot the note that explains your demands, your disguise keeps falling off, or you have a cold and you can't stop sneezing!
- The bank teller should respond to each mishap.

SPARKS: *Did you get away with it? Maybe the bank teller feels sorry for you and helps you out! How and when do things usually go wrong? Are you paying attention to what you are doing?*

How good a listener are you?

- Clap a short rhythm of five beats and ask a friend to clap the same rhythm after you.
- Then, have your friend clap the rhythm again adding a sixth beat.
- Now you repeat this rhythm.
- Then do it again, but add yet another beat.
- Go back and forth each adding a beat to the rhythm.
- See how many beats you can add before someone makes a mistake.

SPARKS: *Add speed to the contest. With each pass make the rhythm get faster and faster. Make sure you keep the same pattern even though you are getting faster.*

What if you were caught inside a mirror and had to reflect the image of anyone in front of you?

- Stand about two feet away from a friend and face each other. Your friend should begin to move in slow motion while you reflect the same motions as closely as possible.
- Work together to make it look as if you are both moving at the same time.
- Don't speak—it will only distract you.
- After a few minutes, switch roles and let your friend reflect your movements.

SPARKS: *When others watch you and your partner, can they tell who is the leader? When you are the reflection where do you focus your eyes to be able to notice all of the different movements that the leader is making?*

What if your job was to clean the bottom of an elephant trainer's shoes? Yuk! Or maybe you're a worm shampooer.

- Decide what the worst job in the world would be.
- You pretend to be new on the job and your friend has to train you.
- Don't talk about it beforehand, just jump right into the scene! You really need this job—you can't quit!

SPARKS: *Your friend should use pantomime to train you. Make your friend take you through all the steps of the job and give you helpful tips. Once you have been trained, try it out and see what you can do. Don't be afraid to make mistakes and have your friend help you do it.*

How long do you think you can stay still?

- Stand across from a friend and try to be perfectly still for as long as possible.
- Eventually, one of you will move.
- At that point, the other one can make a similar movement.
- If your friend moves a little bit, you can move any part of your body a little bit. If you move in a big way, your friend can move any part of his body in a big way.
- Keep reacting to every action—but keep *trying* to stay still.

SPARKS: *How long did it take before one of you moved? Don't argue about who moved first—just react with a motion of your own. Did you ever realize how hard it is to stay still? Try adding a sound to the movements you make when you react to your friend's movements.*

Do you think you know your friends pretty well?

- Pretend that you are a television reporter and interview a friend.
- Find out everything you can about her life. What is she interested in? What does she like to do? Has she ever won a contest or an award? What does she think the future holds?
- Keep the interview moving and you might just learn something about your friend that you never knew.

SPARKS: *Try the interview again. This time focus in on the most interesting part of what you learned about your friend. Ask more questions to get as many details as you can. Prepare a short introduction and a wrap-up as if you are part of a big news program.*

How does your face look when you feel happy or sad or excited?

- Sit across from your friend and with only your face try to show an emotion.
- Think about a time or an event that made you feel that way and let that feeling come out on your face.
- Have your friend guess what emotion you're showing.

SPARKS: *Was your friend right? How could you have been more clear? (Try practicing in front of a mirror.) Go back and forth showing emotions with only your faces. Don't use any words and try not to exaggerate your face. Instead, try to really feel the emotion inside and let your expression reflect it.*

Do you give much thought to your toes?

- Lie flat on your back with your eyes closed.
- Concentrate on your feet. Relax them.
- With every breath you take become more and more relaxed.
- Taking your time, move up your body and relax each and every muscle. Relax your ankles, knees, hips, back, shoulders, arms, neck, face, and everything in between!
- Now slowly open your eyes and stand up. Are you completely relaxed?

SPARKS: *What parts of your body were touching the floor? After you stood up, how did you feel? Did you have more energy or less? Could you jump up fast or did you get up slowly?*

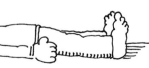

How much can you tell about someone just from the way they sit?
- Sit in a chair and try to show your friend the way that people in different professions might sit.
- How would a ballet dancer sit? How would a pilot sit? How about a typist, a doctor, or a teacher? No talking!

SPARKS: *Were some professions harder to guess than others? Remember, try to make the actions as clear as possible. The clearer the actions the easier it will be to guess the job.*

Do you think well on your feet?
- Start telling a story.
- You have fifteen seconds to begin the story and then you must stop talking and your friend must continue the story from where you left off. Your friend then has fifteen seconds before you become the storyteller again.
- Go back and forth until the story comes to an end.

SPARKS: *Make sure your story has a beginning where you introduce the characters and the setting. Also, be sure that your story has a problem and a solution. Fifteen seconds is not very long, but try not to go over your time limit—it makes the story more fun!*

Have you ever held a baby in your arms? How was that different than holding a book or a cup of hot cocoa?

- Take a scarf and tie a knot at one end of it.
- Pass the scarf to a friend and tell him what you are passing.
- Your friend should receive the scarf as the object you have chosen. Then he picks a new object for the scarf to represent and passes it back to you.
- Before you pass it back to him, take some time to use the object or relate to what you have been passed.

SPARKS: *How can you make your friend believe what you hold in your arms is real? Use your face and voice to show us what you are holding. Can you show the difference between holding a two-day-old kitten and a very breakable vase?*

EASY AS 1, 2, 3

55

How does your voice change when you're angry or tired or happy?

- Using only numbers as dialogue (no other words), carry on a very dramatic conversation with a friend.
- Act out a scene with big gestures, facial expressions, and an expressive voice.
- Can your friend tell how you are feeling? Your scene should have a beginning, middle, and end.

SPARKS: *What happened when you couldn't use real words? How can you make the scene more dramatic? Use your facial expressions and tone of voice.*

SET THE SCENE

GOING UP?

Have you ever felt trapped?

- Pretend that you run into a friend in an elevator.
- Decide what kind of building you're in.
- How many floors are there? Which floor are you going to? Is your friend going to the same place or a different place?
- Begin a conversation in the elevator. Suddenly the elevator gets stuck between floors.
- Work together to get out of this sticky situation.

SPARKS: *Make sure that the way you solve the problem of the stuck elevator is by both you and your friend working together. Show with your body and movements that you are in a small space and are very nervous about getting out.*

Have you ever gone to a friend's house for dinner and they served something that you thought was totally disgusting? What did you do? Did you pretend that you liked it or did you hide it in your pocket?

- Pretend that a friend has invited you to lunch.
- Your friend looks like a regular human being, but is really an alien and chooses very strange combinations of foods to eat.
- You must eat the lunch and try not to show your friend how much you hate it!

SPARKS: *How many emotions can you show on your face at the same time? Try to show sadness in your eyes and happiness in your mouth. Then switch your face and show a sad mouth with happy eyes. What other combinations of emotions can you show on your face?*

There are two sides to every story. Maybe the big bad wolf had a reason for eating the three little pigs.

- Pretend that you are the wolf on the witness stand at your own trial. Your friend is the prosecuting attorney.
- What do you have to say for yourself?
- This is your only chance to speak in your own defense, so make it good!

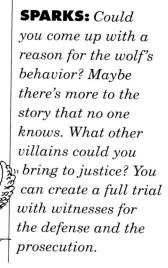

SPARKS: *Could you come up with a reason for the wolf's behavior? Maybe there's more to the story that no one knows. What other villains could you bring to justice? You can create a full trial with witnesses for the defense and the prosecution.*

VEGETABLE STEREO 59

Did you ever think about how funny some words sound?

- Sit facing a friend.
- Begin by slowly saying the name of any vegetable you can think of. Make sure you speak v-e-r-y s-l-o-w-l-y, as if you are speaking in slow motion.
- Your friend should try to say the vegetable name at the same time. The goal is for both of you to speak together without your friend knowing in advance what you are about to say.
- Take turns leading and following.

SPARKS: *Concentrate on your friend's mouth. How can you tell what she is about to say? Are vegetables with long or short names easier? Try the same game naming colors, states, or flowers. What else could you name?*

Have you ever wanted to be famous?
- Pick a celebrity or historical figure and take on their identity.
- Your friend has three minutes to interview you and try to guess who you are.
- Be sure you answer your friend's questions in the first person ("I am . . . ," "I think . . . ").

SPARKS: *When you take on the secret identity, try to act just like the person you're pretending to be. How would that person sit, talk, and laugh?*

What's the craziest thing anyone has ever done for you?

- You and a friend decide on a place to be.
- Make it some place that would lend itself to conversation. You might choose an art museum, a bookstore, or a school lunchroom.
- You have three minutes to convince your friend that you must have his shoes.
- Your friend would rather keep his shoes, of course, and tries to talk you out of it.

SPARKS: *Make sure you only take three minutes for this game. Try the same idea with other crazy situations. Maybe you need to get your friend to cluck like a chicken or pretend to be a teapot. You'd better have a pretty good reason!*

Are you good at noticing details?
- Sit on the floor facing a friend.
- Now you turn around and have your friend change four things about the way he looks. Your friend might tuck in a collar, take off a shoe, roll up a sleeve, or change his watch to the other arm.
- When your friend is ready, turn around and give yourself thirty seconds to notice what's been changed.

SPARKS: *Which changes were easy to spot? Which were hard? Why? Try this several times and see if you get better at guessing after you've played for a while.*

ON THE AIR

63

Would you tell a story differently if you were talking on the phone rather than in person? Is it harder to communicate when your friend can't see your face?

- Pretend that you are conducting a radio broadcast.
- Take a story that you and a friend are very familiar with.
- Using only your voice and sound effects, perform the story with as much expression as possible.
- Make your words as colorful as possible.

SPARKS: *Think of all the sound effects that you could add to your story. What sounds can you make using your voice or objects to make your story more interesting? Can some sounds replace words in your story?*

What if someone cast a spell on you so that every time you opened your mouth only singing came out?

- Pick a story that everyone knows well, like Little Red Riding Hood or The Three Bears.
- Decide who will play each part and then sing the story.
- Act out the scene while you sing it.
- Make sure you don't speak any lines!

SPARKS: *Remember, it doesn't matter if you have a lousy voice for this game—just sing! Did you change your voice for each character you played? Goldilocks shouldn't sound like Papa Bear. What would it be like if you sang everything in your everyday life?*

Have you ever tasted a peanut butter and ketchup sandwich? Some things just don't seem to go together.

- You and a friend each select an object without showing it to each other.
- Show your objects at the same time and then give yourselves two minutes to figure out a situation where both objects could work together.

SPARKS: *Try to select the craziest objects that you can find. Then think of a place and a reason for these things to be together. Try not to rehearse your scene or start over. Remember to work with your friend to create something together.*

FREEZE!

How fast can you stop?

- Put on some music and start to dance. Have a friend control the music.
- When the music stops, no matter what position you're in, you must freeze.
- Wherever you are, don't move a muscle. Don't even blink! Keep your balance and don't fall over.
- How long can you hold the pose?

SPARKS: *When you freeze, try focusing your eyes on a spot on the floor about three feet in front of you—it will help you keep your balance. Make sure you freeze as soon as the music stops. If you are jumping in mid-air, land first—then freeze.*

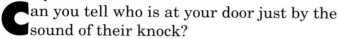**an you tell who is at your door just by the sound of their knock?

- Pick a door in your house and you and a friend stand on opposite sides.
- With the door closed, take turns knocking on the door.
- Use the knock to show different feelings.
- How would your knock sound if you were angry, sad, happy, frightened, or any other feeling you can think of?
- Guess the feelings behind each knock.

SPARKS: *Try to transfer the same feelings into other everyday activities. How would brushing your teeth look if you were very angry? What would eating cereal look like if you were very happy?*

Have you ever had your fortune told? Did you believe the prediction?

- Pretend that you are a fortune-teller.
- Have your friend pretend to be a familiar fairy-tale character at the beginning of their story.
- Try to convince Papa Bear that soon a little girl will break into his house, break one of his chairs and eat his food.
- Try to convince an old emperor that he will one day walk through the streets of town in his underwear!

SPARKS: *Use all of the information you can to persuade the character of the events that will happen. They should have a hard time believing it.*

Can you make the sound of a creaking door or a dripping faucet?

- Pretend that you are asleep in your bed and it is time to get up.
- Walk into your imaginary bathroom and, using pantomime, wash your face, brush your teeth and fix your hair.
- At the same time have your friend make exaggerated sound effects to go with your actions.

SPARKS: *Make sure your friend tries to make the sound effects happen at the same time you are doing the actions. React to the sounds. What other activities can you act out while your friend supplies the sound?*

If you could change five things about the world, what would they be?

- You are the ruler of the world and your friend is your recording secretary.
- You are about to give a speech announcing your changes. No classes on Fridays! In-line skating permitted in school hallways! What would you change?
- Have your friend write all of your ideas down and question you about the details.
- Then make a short speech about why you are changing these things.

SPARKS: *Make sure that you speak with conviction. If you make these changes will everyone be happy with them? Who might not be happy? Have your friend represent the people who would be opposed to your changes. Can you compromise and find a change that would make everyone happy?*

Have you ever watched a film in reverse?

- Pick a location and an activity. You might choose skiing down a hill or fishing in a pond.
- You and a friend should act out this activity—backwards!
- Start at the end of the activity and go backwards, as if someone were rewinding a film of you.
- When you get to the beginning of the activity, go through it again, this time moving forward and in slow motion.
- Then try it again going backwards.

SPARKS: *Did you think of more things that you could add to the activity when you were going through it forward in slow motion? Try writing down all the elements of your activity so you won't leave anything out. Work on controlling each motion and keeping a steady pace.*

Is your local weather reporter serious and dignified or kind of zany? What kind of weather reporter would you be?

- Make up a weather report with any kind of weather that you want.
- Using props around the house, your friend must quickly act out every type of weather you describe.
- Whatever your friend does, make sure you continue the report without missing a beat.
  You might want to wear a raincoat and do this outside!

SPARKS: *How can you make it snow? In the movies they use instant potato flakes. Hoses can create rain. And a magazine, waved back and forth, can make a nice breeze. Don't forget the sound effects!*

Do you believe in aliens? What would they be like?

- Make up a name for an imaginary planet.
- What kinds of creatures live on this planet? How do they walk, talk, eat, or ride bikes? Do they even have bikes?
- Pretend that you are one of these aliens and you've come to explore the planet Earth. What will you need to bring with you from your home planet? What will seem especially strange to you on Earth? What might be familiar?

SPARKS: *Ask your friend to be the first Earth creature that you come across in your explorations. Would you be afraid of each other? How will you communicate?*

Do you talk to yourself? What do you say?

- Act out an everyday, ordinary activity like taking a shower or brushing your teeth.
- Have a friend guess what might be going through your mind and say it out loud as you continue to act.
- Have your face react to what your friend says.
- Pretend you are actually thinking those thoughts.

SPARKS: *What really does go through your mind when you are alone? Pay attention to what you are thinking when you do everyday activities. Are you thinking about what you're doing? What do you think other people think about when they do the same sorts of things?*

Did you ever wish that you could wave a magic wand to solve your problems?

- Make up a situation where there is a conflict that could only be solved by magic.
- Then you become the magician!
- Explain your magical powers to your friend and then decide how it will affect the story. Maybe the magic only makes the situation worse!

SPARKS: *What kind of magic did you pick? Three wishes? Fairy godmother? Magic stone? Are there any limitations or rules to this magic?*

When was the last time you had a tug-of-war? Remember how it felt to pull with all your might? What did your face look like? How was your body positioned?

- Pick up an imaginary rope, give one end of it to a friend and have an imaginary tug-of-war.
- Use your body and face to show that you are using all of your strength and concentration in the contest.
- Work with your friend to make sure that it is a rope you are pulling and not a big rubber band!
- When your friend pulls you give a little and when you pull your friend must give a little.

SPARKS: *Who won? Did you lose your balance when you lost? Did the winner cheer, or was he too worn out from the game? Try the game again with something other than a rope. Maybe this time you are using a big rubber band.*

What do you say when you greet a friend? "What's Up?" "Hey!" What do you say when you greet an older relative that you haven't seen for a long time?

• Show your friend a greeting and have her guess who you are greeting and how you feel about that person.

SPARKS: *Try the same greetings using letters of the alphabet in place of words. Show how you feel with just the tone of your voice, your expressions, and the way your body moves. See if your friend can still guess who you're greeting.*

Don't other people's chores always seem easier than yours?

- You and a friend should each pick a chore, but don't tell each other what you've chosen. (Try raking leaves, shoveling snow, watering plants, washing dishes, or any chore you might do around the house.)
- Without using any props, you should both pretend to do your chores at the same time.
- Without stopping, try to figure out what your friend is doing.
- As soon as you have both figured out what the other is doing, exchange jobs.

SPARKS: *You can play this more competitively: As soon as one of you figures out what the other is doing you can switch to their job. Whoever catches on first wins the round. Then you can start over with two new chores.*

CONDUCT A TEST

CONDUCT A TEST 79

How well do you follow directions?

- Stand across from a friend and begin counting to ten, in a medium volume, over and over again.
- Your friend should direct you just as a conductor directs an orchestra.
- As your friend makes larger hand movements, your voice should get louder. When the movements get smaller, your voice gets softer.

SPARKS: *Make sure you watch the conductor very closely. How many different sound levels can you create? How fast can you change your sound level? Play with all of the different levels of your voice.*

WHAT TIME IS IT? 80

Did you ever think about all the things that happen in the same place at different times of the day?

- Think about your kitchen table. All day and night different kinds of things happen there.
- Pick a place and show, in three very short scenes, things that might happen there at three different times of the day. You might choose an elevator or the front stairs of an apartment building.
- Take a few minutes to set each scene and figure out who you're going to be, then jump right in!

SPARKS: *You don't have to play the same character in each scene. There are probably lots of different people that come through this place. Try to select activities that are very different from each other. What can you do at a table other than eat?*

What's your favorite song?

- Select a song that you and your friend know very well.
- You sing the first word of the song, then your friend sings the second, and you sing the third, and so on until the end. Make sure you don't sing a word together.
- Try to make the song seem like one voice is singing it.

SPARKS: *Try the song again, but this time stand back to back so you cannot see your friend's face. How is this different from the first time you sang? Which was more of a challenge?*

What if you swallowed your clock radio and had to have an operation to get it out of your stomach?

- Pretend that you are a world-famous surgeon preparing for surgery. Your friend is the patient.
- Scrub your hands, then put on your gown, gloves, and mask.
- With your imaginary scalpel, open up the patient and, using pantomime, pull out the craziest thing you can think of.
- Show it to your patient and see if she can guess what she has swallowed!

SPARKS: *Remember, the goal is for your friend to guess what you pulled out of her. Try to be as clear as possible about the object. Is the object heavy? Run your hand around the edges of the object. What will your face look like when you pull this thing out of your friend's stomach?*

IMAGINATION STATION

Have you ever seen a commercial that was more entertaining than the television show it was interrupting?

- Think of a new product and then make up a commercial that you and your friend can perform to sell it. Some commercials use side-by-side comparisons or celebrity endorsements. Others are about how you will feel if you use the product.
- Watch some commercials and see what strategy would work for your product.

SPARKS: *If you have a video camera you might want to tape your commercial and see yourselves on TV. After you've done your first commercial, make up a brand-new product that will be invented fifty years from now. Then, make up a commercial for the twenty-first century.*

What can you change about the way you move? You can change the direction you are moving. You can change your speed and go faster or slower. You can also change your level by getting up on your toes or down on your knees or anywhere in between.

- You and your friend should walk around in a small space without walking in circles and without bumping into each other.
- Take turns deciding what you should change about the way you are moving: level, speed, or direction.

SPARKS: *Remember to only change one thing at a time! As you play for a little while, start to change things faster. Try to change your movements at the exact time that the new change is announced.*

Have you ever met someone who knows you, but you don't remember him?

- Without telling your friend, select a type of relationship (mother and daughter, brothers, cousins, teacher and student), then choose which part you will play.
- Begin to talk to your friend as if you both have the relationship you chose.
- Keep going until your friend catches on and can respond in a way that lets you know he understands how you're related.

SPARKS: *How do different people talk to you? Take a day and listen to what people say and how they say it. Write down some of the feelings that you remember about each exchange. Then, use these feelings and play this game again. See if you can use what you observed to make the relationships clearer.*

What if you had to follow orders, no matter how outrageous they were?

- Ask your friend to pretend to be the ruler of a kingdom.
- You are her servant and must obey her commands. Maybe you are sent out into the wilderness to pluck a tail feather from the exotic yucca bird.
- Your friend must describe exactly what you must do to complete the task.
- You should use imaginary props to follow her commands.

SPARKS: *Encourage your friend to make up really outrageous and crazy activities for you to act out. Try the game again and this time ask your friend to describe the activity much faster. Can you keep up?*

Do you have a good memory?

- You and a friend should each take a tray and gather about twelve small objects to put on it: a sponge, comb, napkin, salt shaker, candle, anything you have around the house. Don't let your friend see what you're choosing.
- When you're both ready, show each other your trays for only fifteen seconds and then put them out of sight.
- You now have sixty seconds to write down everything that you can remember from your friend's tray.

SPARKS: *When the minute is up, look at the trays and see what you forgot. What kinds of things did you leave off your list? Can you figure out why? What kinds of things were easy to remember?*

Have you ever looked at a picture or a painting and wondered about the people in it?

- Look through a book or a magazine with a friend and find a picture with two people in it.
- Decide who will play which role and then bring the picture to life.
- Who are you? Where are you? What are you doing? What are you talking about?

SPARKS: *Make sure you keep the scene short and exciting. Don't just talk about the weather. Make it dramatic! Have some big event happen that you need to react to!*

RHYME TIME

Can you think of a word that rhymes with orange?

- Sit across from a friend and have a rhyming contest.
- You say a word and then your friend has to say another word that rhymes with it.
- Then you say a third word that rhymes with the first two.
- Keep going back and forth until you run out of rhymes.
- Then pick a new word and start again.

SPARKS: *Make sure that you use real words! You might want to have a dictionary handy to settle disputes. Which are easier to rhyme, long or short words?*

Would you walk into your bedroom the same way you walk into the principal's office?

- Stand behind an imaginary door.
- Open it and walk into a place.
- Without using your voice or any props, show where you are by your expressions and the activities you choose to do.
- Have your friend guess where you have just arrived.

SPARKS: *What kind of expression will be on your face when you walk into this place? Are you happy to be there? Is it a scary place? Is there somebody there that you want to see?*

What's more important—what you say or how you say it?

- Take a nursery rhyme that you are very familiar with and say it in the following ways: as if describing a mystery, as if you are really bored, as if you are reading a recipe, as if you are very nervous, as if you are terrified.
- Have a friend listen and try to guess the way you are performing the rhyme.

SPARKS: *What happens to the meaning of the rhyme when you change the way you say it? Think of other ways to say the rhyme and see if your friend can guess the feeling behind it.*

Are you a sports fan?

- With a friend, decide what kind of sporting event you are watching and pretend that you are cheering for your team.
- Have your faces and bodies show whether your team is winning or losing.
- Make the game exciting and make sure that you and your friend are both watching the same game and cheering at the same time.
- Then have the game come to an end and show us who won.

SPARKS: *Try watching the game again, but this time have your friend cheer for the opposite team. So, when you are cheering, your friend is booing!*

THE OBJECT OF THE GAME 93

The object of this game is to identify objects that you have around the house. Easy? Not if you're blindfolded!

- You wear a blindfold and your friend hands you objects to identify.
- If you can't guess what something is, your friend can give you a hint by telling you in what room you would normally find the object.

SPARKS: *Could you tell which objects you were holding right away? Which were easier to guess? Why?*

WORLD TRAVELER

94

Have you ever traveled to a country where the people did not speak your language? How did you communicate?

- Pretend that your friend is a storekeeper in a foreign country.
- You want to buy something from the store, but you don't see it on the shelf, so you have to ask for it. But the storekeeper doesn't speak English and can't understand you.
- With hand and body motions, explain what you need.

SPARKS: *Did you find yourself talking or making sounds to communicate with the storekeeper even though he couldn't understand? Try the game again and pretend you are on the phone with the storekeeper. Can you communicate using only sounds?*

When you're playing catch, you've got to keep your eye on the ball, right? But what if the ball was invisible and its size and weight kept changing?

- Pick up an imaginary ball and see it in your hand. Show by the way you hold the ball how big it is and how much it weighs.
- Now throw the ball to a friend who catches it and then changes its size and weight. Your friend then throws the new ball back to you.
- Keep changing the ball and throwing it back and forth.

SPARKS: *How does the way you catch a ball change depending upon its size and weight? Try tossing a heavy (real) ball back and forth in slow motion. Be aware of how you are standing. Are your knees bent? Do you step forward when you throw? Do you use both hands to catch?*

How many different voices do each of us have inside? You may have more than you think. How would different characters say the same sentence?

- Take the line "Please pass the ketchup." How would you say this line? How would an old man say this line? How about a baby? A police officer?
- Choose a character to say this line. Don't tell your friend who you've selected.
- Have your friend try to guess who you are, just from one sentence.

SPARKS: *What would it sound like if you were speaking as a witch or a wolf? Discover all the voices you have inside.*

Everybody has a rhythm to the way they speak.

- Say your name out loud and have your friend repeat it in the same rhythm.
- Both of you clap the rhythm of the name.
- Try making up some movement to match the rhythm of your name. For instance, the name Lisa has two beats. Lisa might choose to wave her arm back and forth to fill her name's rhythm.
- Next learn the rhythm and body movement for your friend's name.
- Now try putting your names together, adding on until you have a little dance.

SPARKS: *After your dance is complete, try it again without saying the names at the same time. Just say the names in your head. Were you both together? Try it faster! This game is fun with big groups too.*

When we ride in a car or a bus we usually don't pay attention to how our bodies move when the car turns or stops.

- Sit side by side with a friend and pretend that you are riding in a car. Whoever sits on the left should drive.
- Your body should move differently when the car is moving than when the car stops.
- Which way does your body lean when the car turns right or left?
- Try to carry on a conversation while you're riding.

SPARKS: *Make sure you and your friend move the same way at the same time, since you are both riding in the same car! How can you show whether you are driving on a residential street or a highway? How could you use your body to show that the car has gone out of control?*

IN A WORD

Does it take you a long time to tell a story? Sometimes all you need is one word.

- Take one word and build an entire scene around it. For example, think of a situation where you would have occasion to say the word "applesauce."
- You and a friend perform a short scene to show where you are and what you are doing. Don't say any other words except "applesauce."
- Come up with as many different "applesauce" situations as possible.

APPLESAUCE!

SPARKS: *Pick some other words and see how many scenes you can come up with for them. Make some of your scenes serious and some of them crazy. Make sure that they're not too long and that the spoken word comes at the end of the scene.*